Santa Mouse
COLORING AND PENCIL PUZZLE BOOK

By MICHAEL BROWN
Illustrated by NINA BARBARESI
Cover art by ELFRIEDA DEWITT

© 1998, 2000 by Michael Brown Enterprises

This 2010 edition published by Sandy Creek, by arrangement with Michael Brown Enterprises.

Sandy Creek
122 Fifth Avenue
New York, NY 10011

ISBN: 978-1-4351-2897-2

Printed and bound in Canada
Manufactured 07/10

Lot #:
1 3 5 7 9 10 8 6 4 2

A tiny mouse lives here.

The mouse has no name.

Come in for a visit.

The mouse cleans house.

He washes his clothes.

The mouse looks for food.

He likes to eat fruit.

Cake! What a treat!

In winter the mouse plays in the snow.

Hello, Mr. Squirrel.

blue jay

The winter birds are friendly.

sparrow

chickadee

cardinal

The mouse goes ice-skating.

Sometimes he goes sledding.

It's time to get ready for Christmas.

Look who's sitting in the Christmas wreath!

The mouse decorates his tree.

It's Christmas Eve.

What is the mouse looking for?

A present for Santa!

Paper from chewing gum is useful.

He leaves the present near the tree.

The mouse gets ready for bed.

He brushes his teeth.

The mouse climbs into bed.

He dreams that Santa finds his gift.

A dream come true.

"I will call you Santa Mouse," says Santa.

Special clothes for Santa's new helper.

Santa Mouse looks just right.

Santa puts his helper in the sleigh.

The reindeer are ready to go.

On, Dasher! On, Prancer!

Santa Mouse goes everywhere with Santa.

They stop at a small house in the woods...

and a big house in town.

They visit a ranch in the desert...

and a cottage by the sea.

Santa Mouse is a good helper.

He brushes the teddy bear.

Santa brings wonderful presents.

Time out for cookies and milk.

Back to work!

What a long night!

Santa takes his helper home.

Goodnight, Santa. Merry Christmas!

SANTA MOUSE
❧ Pencil Puzzle Fun ❧

Based on the book SANTA MOUSE

by Michael Brown

Activities by Arlene Block
Illustrated by Nina Barbaresi
Cover art by Elfrieda DeWitt

BARNES & NOBLE BOOKS
NEW YORK

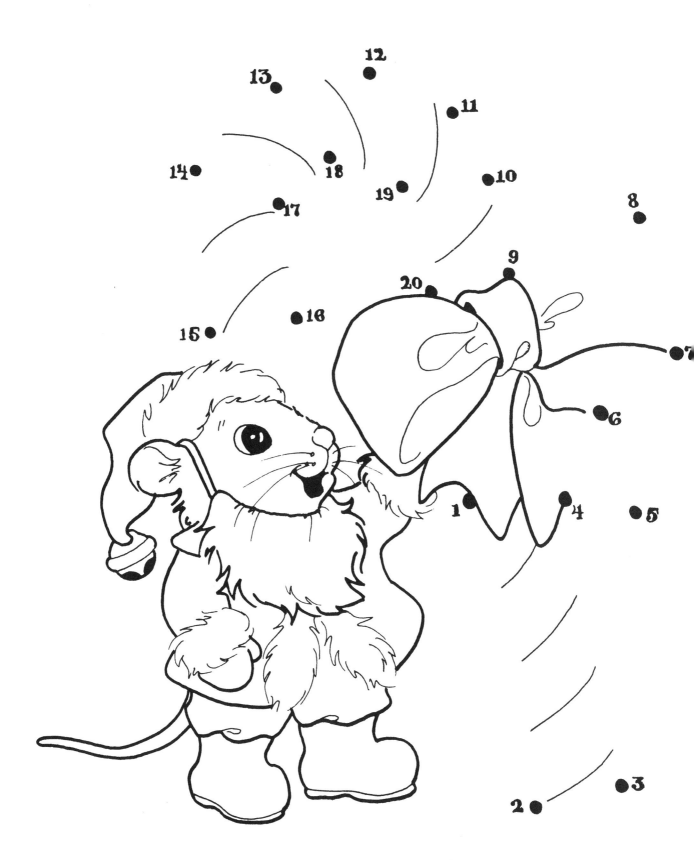

A Sweet Surprise

Follow the dots from one to twenty, and you will find
a Christmas treat for Santa Mouse.

Santa's Helper

Color the picture of Santa Mouse.

Where's Santa?

Draw a line through the busy workshop to help Santa Mouse find Santa. (The answers to this and the other puzzles are at the end of this book.)

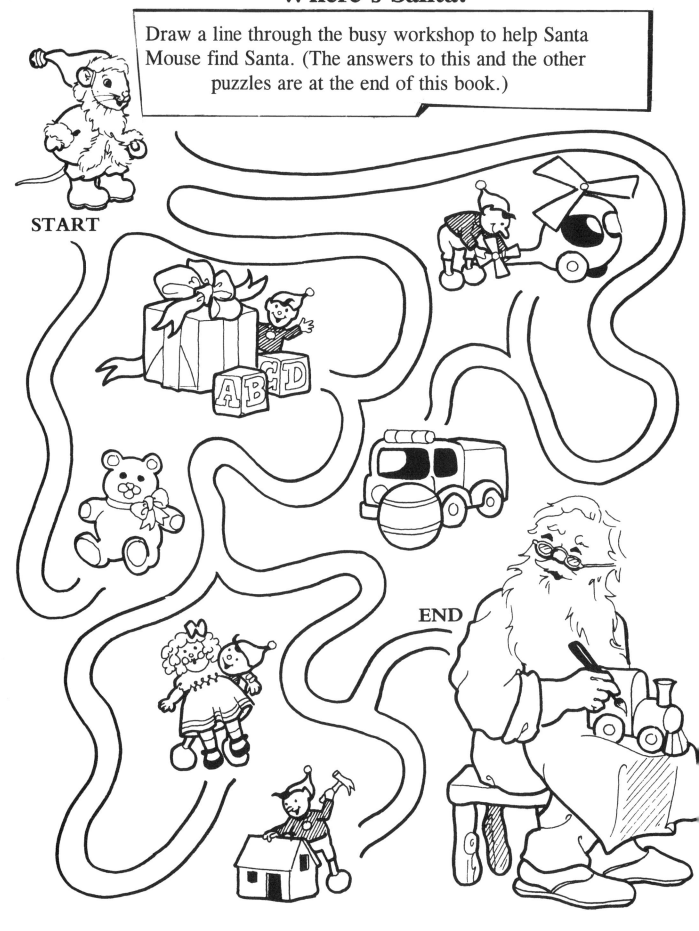

START

END

Look Closely

Draw a circle around the picture in each row that does not belong with the others.

Santa's Here

The letters that spell SANTA are hidden in the picture. Can you find all five letters? Find the letter A two times.

Dressing Up

What should Santa Mouse wear when he rides in these special vehicles? Draw a line from each vehicle to Santa Mouse dressed in the right clothes.

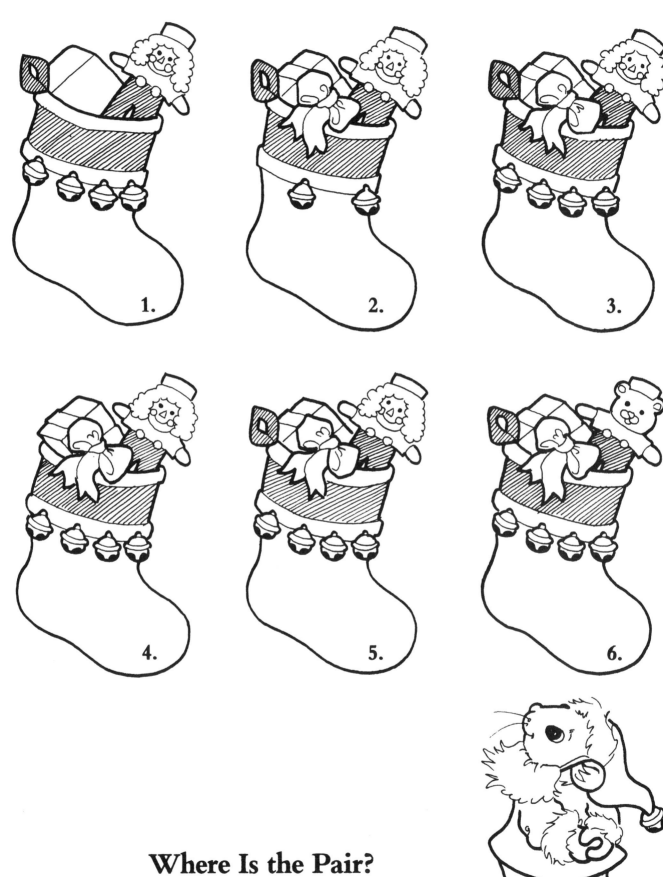

Where Is the Pair?

Which two Christmas stockings
are exactly alike?

Hiding in the Snow

There are five objects hidden in the picture: a fish, a fork, an ice cream cone, a pencil, and a candle. Can you find all five objects?

What's in the Box?

To find out what is inside the big box, color each space that has a dot in it.

Crazy Christmas Tree

Santa Mouse has put six things on the tree that don't belong there. Can you find all six?

Santa Mouse Cleans House

Which picture of Santa Mouse is different
from the others?

Here Comes Santa Mouse!

Can you find six rectangles on Santa Mouse's train?
Color the rectangles and then color the rest of the
picture.

END

START

What a Clutter!

Santa's helper can't find the Christmas presents he hid in
the attic. Draw a path from Santa Mouse to the gifts.

Are They the Same?

These two pictures are not exactly alike. Can you find six things that are different?

Santa Mouse's Favorite Place

Where is Santa Mouse? To find out, follow the dots from one to eighteen.

Two by Two

Draw a line from each cookie at the left to a matching cookie at the right.

What's Up?

To find out why Santa Mouse looks surprised, color the picture in the following way. Spaces marked 1 are red, 2 is blue, 3 is green, and 4 is yellow.

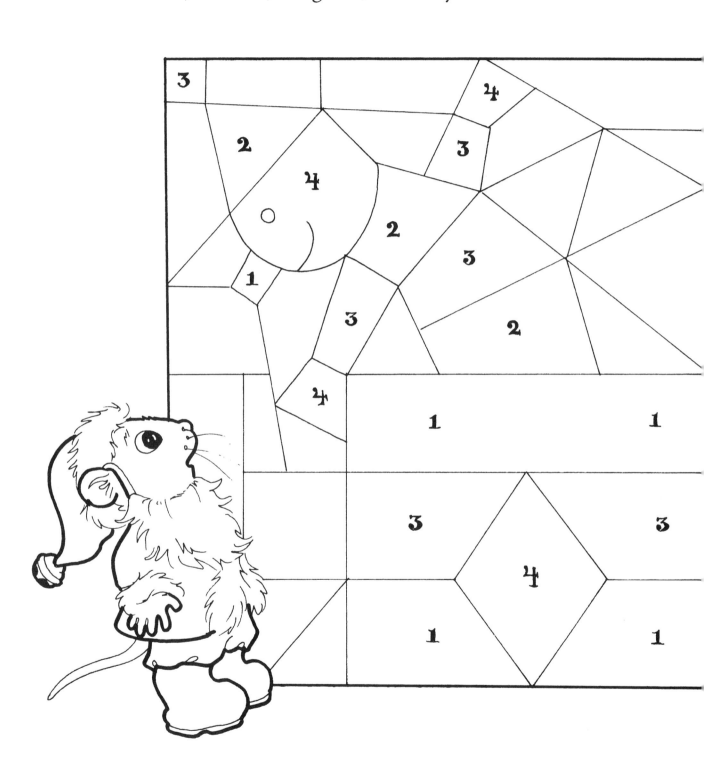

B Is for Bedtime

Can you find seven things in Santa Mouse's room that begin with the letter B?

What's Cooking?

There are six silly things happening in Santa Mouse's kitchen. Can you find all six?

Christmas Is Here

Can you find all the letters that spell CHRISTMAS in Santa Mouse's wreath? Find the letter S two times. Circle the letters as you find them.

A Mystery Gift

Each picture on Santa Mouse's gift tag stands for a letter. Write the correct letter under each picture, and you will know who the present is for!

= A   = R

= T   = O

= N   = F

= S

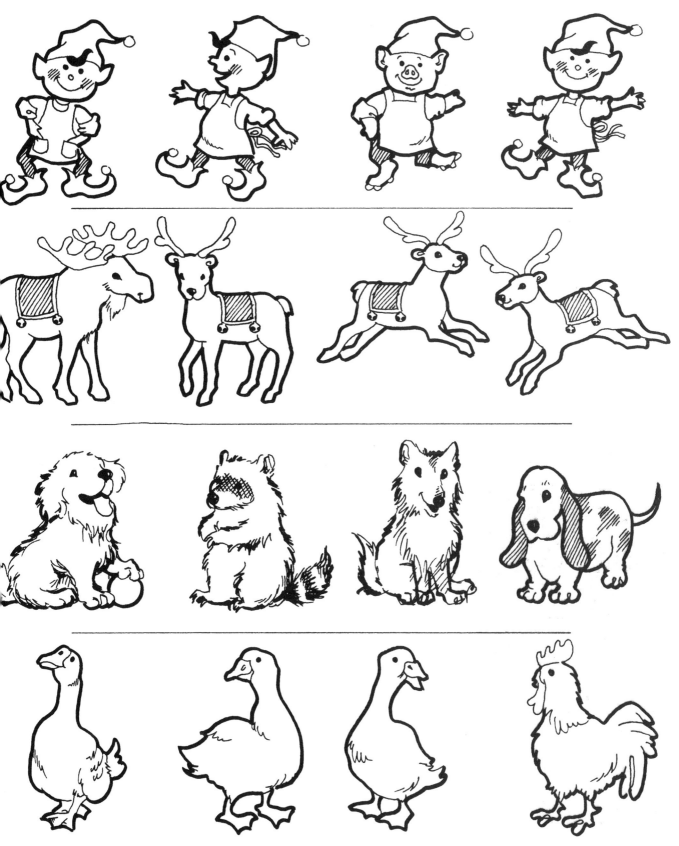

Which One Is Different?

Circle the picture in each row that doesn't belong with the others.

Are the Angels the Same?

Only two of the Christmas angels are exactly alike.
Can you find them?

Who's There?

To find out what kind of animal this is, color each space that has a dot in it.

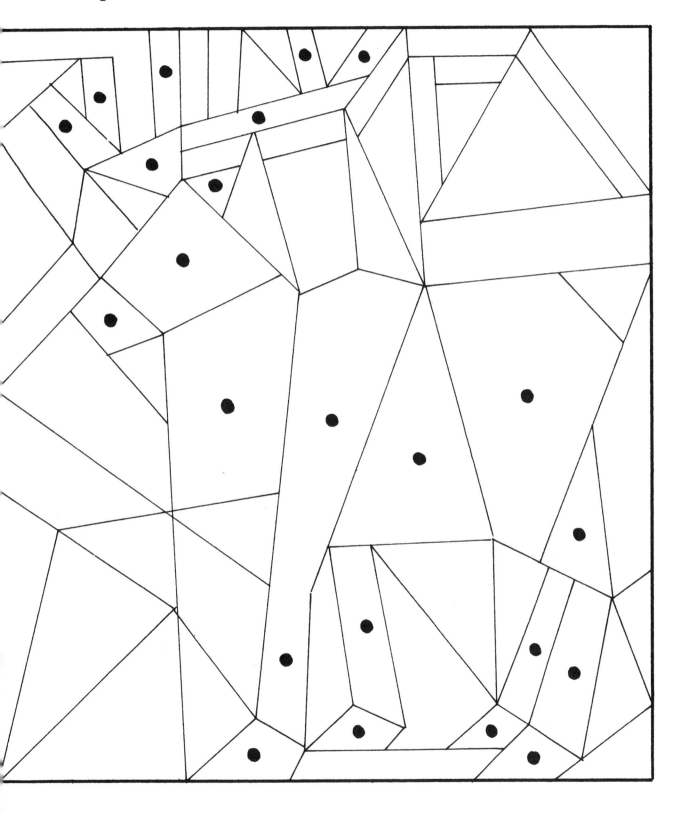

Santa Mouse Needs Help!

Santa Mouse can't find his hat. You can find it for him.
Start at Santa Mouse and draw a line—

1. to the bed
2. to the teddy bear
3. to the bookcase
4. to the toy chest
5. to the tree
6. and back to Santa Mouse

A-mazing Tangle

Santa Mouse is surrounded by a tangle of Christmas trimmings. Draw a line to show him the way out.

EXIT

Are They the Same?

The two pictures of Santa Mouse are not exactly alike. Can you find five things that are different?

Rag Dolls All Around

Each rag doll in the picture has a twin. Can you find four pairs of rag dolls? Draw a line to connect them.

Silly Winter Riddles

Why do birds fly south in winter?
(It's too far to walk.)

What has a thumb but only one finger?
(A mitten.)

What kind of toe has no foot?
(Mistletoe.)

What is Tarzan's favorite Christmas song?
(Jungle Bells.)

Santa Mouse's Dinner

Can you find eight circles in the picture? Color the circles, and then color the rest of the picture.

Fix the Picture

A part of each reindeer is missing. Draw each missing part, and then color the rest of the picture.

Winter Words

Santa Mouse and his friend are playing in the snow. Can you find seven winter words hidden in the picture?

Santa Mouse's Music

There are eight triangles in this picture. Color the triangles, and then color the rest of the picture.

Mittens for a Mouse

Find two mittens that match, and color them with the same crayon. Then find another pair. There are seven pairs of mittens in all.

All in a Row

Draw a circle around one picture in each row that doesn't belong with the others.

S Is for Santa

Seven presents in Santa's sack have names that begin with the letter S. Can you find all seven?

Snowflakes for Santa Mouse

Draw a line from each snowflake at the left to a matching snowflake at the right.

START

END

Santa Mouse on Skis

Draw a path for Santa Mouse so that he can ski all the way down the mountain.

Ship Ahoy, Santa Mouse!

There are six squares on Captain S. Mouse's boat.
Color the squares, and then color the rest of the
picture.

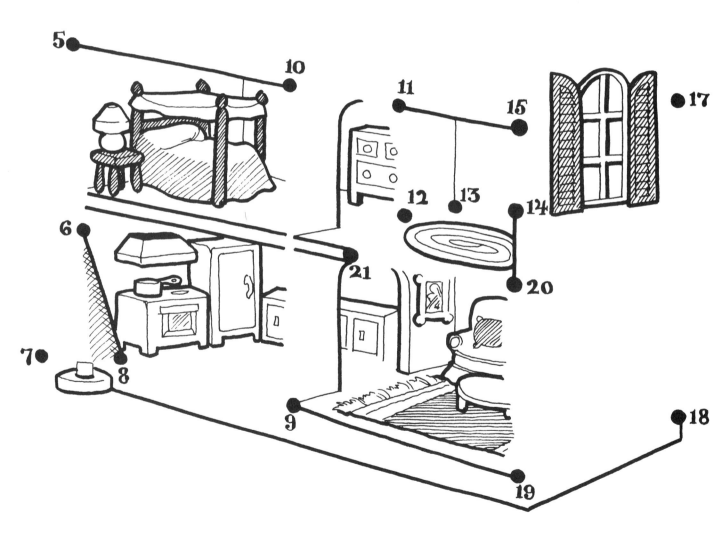

What Is Santa's Helper Making?

To find out what Santa Mouse is building,
just follow the dots.

What a Treat!

There are eight pieces of cheese hidden in the picture.
Can you help Santa Mouse find them?

It's Rhyme Time!

Look at the pictures. Then think of two rhyming words that tell what you see in each picture. Write the rhyming words in the spaces.

1. One _____ on a _____ .

2. Two _____

with _____ .

3. Three _____ on _____ .

4. Four _____ on ____

Good-bye, Santa

Color the picture of Santa Mouse waving good-bye to his friend.

ANSWERS

WHERE'S SANTA?

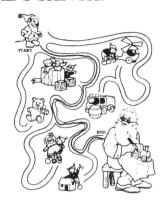

LOOK CLOSELY

SANTA'S HERE

DRESSING UP

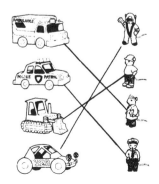

WHERE IS THE PAIR?

Stockings 3 and 5 are alike.

HIDING IN THE SNOW

CRAZY CHRISTMAS TREE

Things that don't belong: comb, brush, carrots, sneaker, toothpaste, and milk carton

SANTA MOUSE CLEANS HOUSE

Picture 5 is different.

WHAT A CLUTTER!

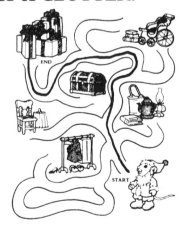

ARE THEY THE SAME?

In the bottom picture, the electric cord is not plugged in. The girl's bow, the cat, and the star on the tree are missing. The doll and the bedroom slipper have been added.

TWO BY TWO

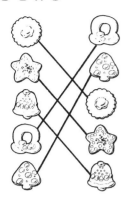

B IS FOR BEDTIME

ball	bear
blanket	boat
bed	book
bell	

WHAT'S COOKING?

The clock is upside down. There's a pear on Santa Mouse's head. There's a spool on the popcorn chain. The chain is dropping into a man's hat. There's a boot in the oven and a Christmas ball in the saucepan.

CHRISTMAS IS HERE

A MYSTERY GIFT

WHICH ONE IS DIFFERENT?

ARE THE ANGELS THE SAME?

Angels 1 and 6 are alike.

AMAZING TANGLE

ARE THEY THE SAME?

The picture at the right has no bell on Santa Mouse's hat. He's winking. He's holding a sprig of holly instead of a candy cane. He has only one boot. The tassles on his jacket are missing.

RAG DOLLS ALL AROUND

WINTER WORDS

Hidden words: HAT, SLED, SKATE, MITTEN, SNOWMAN, SKI, ICE

MITTENS FOR A MOUSE

ALL IN A ROW

S IS FOR SANTA

S presents: SWORD, SPOON, SKATES, SOLDIER, SAILBOAT, SLED, SNOWSHOE

SNOWFLAKES FOR SANTA MOUSE

SANTA MOUSE ON SKIS

WHAT A TREAT

IT'S RHYME TIME!

1. One dog on a log.
2. Two kittens with mittens.
3. Three bees on skis.
4. Four mice on ice.